BRITISH PLANT LIFE   NUMBER 4

MOUNTAIN PLANTS OF THE BRITISH ISLES

AN INTRODUCTION TO OUR NATIVE ARCTIC-ALPINE FLORA

By Heather Pardoe

AMGUEDDFEYDD AC ORIELAU CENEDLAETHOL CYMRU
NATIONAL MUSEUMS & GALLERIES OF WALES

CARDIFF 1995

First published 1995
National Museum of Wales
Cathays Park
Cardiff CF1 3NP

ISBN 0 7200 0423 3

Production: Arwel Hughes
Type: Baskerville 9/10pt
Printing: McLays, Cardiff

Acknowledgements

I am grateful to Gwynn Ellis, Ray Woods, David Mardon, Andrew Martin, Barry Thomas and Roy Perry for their valuable comments on an earlier version of the manuscript. I would like to thank the staff of the Ben Lawers National Nature Reserve, particularly David Mardon, who kindly allowed me to use many of his excellent photographs. Thanks also go to Lynne Farrell, Heather Angel and Peter Russell who contributed photographs. The maps were redrawn by the author with the assistance of Deborah Spillards and Chris Meechan. They are largely based on the distribution maps in *An Atlas of the Wild Flowers of Britain and Northern Europe* (1978) by A. Fitter and *The Hamlyn Photographic Guide to the Wild Flowers of Britain and Northern Europe* (1992) by B. Gibbons and P. Brough. I am also grateful to John Matthews and Chris Caseldine who first stimulated my interest in arctic-alpine plants.

This series of booklets on British Plants produced by the Department of Botany of the National Museum of Wales is an introduction to the abundant plant life to be found in the British Isles. It is the hope of the authors that readers will be left with a greater appreciation of the diversity and beauty of living things and be stimulated to explore further the natural world around them.

Cover photograph: Mountain Avens *(Dryas octopetala)* by D. Parish

Introduction

Plant distribution

This booklet is intended as an introduction to the native mountain plants of the British Isles. These are species that are restricted to high altitude sites, but, as their name suggests, they are much more widespread in the Arctic or in alpine areas of Europe or in many cases both. The precise definition of the term alpine has been hotly debated but, broadly, it refers to a species that has its main distribution above the altitudinal treeline. An arctic species, in contrast, has its main distribution above the latitudinal treeline. A browse through the distribution maps in this booklet reveals that several of the arctic-alpine species have quite distinct distribution patterns; some are found mainly in arctic areas and northern Scandinavia, whereas others are more at home in the mountains of continental Europe such as the Alps and the Pyrenees. Most of the montane vascular plants found in the British Isles occur in the Highlands of Scotland. It has been estimated that of the montane vascular flora of Britain and Ireland, Ireland has 29%, Wales 35%, northern England 52%, but the Scottish Highlands and Islands 93%.

Often a species is restricted to high altitudes at low latitudes but as one moves northwards it is found at progressively lower altitudes, reflecting a correlation with lower temperatures. For example, Purple Saxifrage (*Saxifraga oppositifolia*) is restricted to relatively high altitudes in southern Europe and southern Britain, but in the Shetland Isles it is found at sea level and in the high Arctic it is prolific at all altitudes.

The spatial distribution of individual species reflects their ecological requirements and includes a range of environmental factors such as temperature regime, quantity and distribution of precipitation, duration of snowlie, length of growing season, nutrient requirements, disturbance, soil stability and exposure. Equally important are biological factors such as competition, grazing pressure and human disturbance. One of the most fundamental influences on the distribution of a species is climate.

To fully understand the distribution of arctic-alpine plants we need to consider the enormous changes in the environment that have occurred over the past 20,000 years. Using evidence from pollen and plant remains preserved in peat and lake sediments we can trace dramatic changes in vegetation. At the start of this period massive icesheets covered large areas of the British Isles, the ice extending southwards as far as the Thames. Huge glaciers grew from the edges of these icesheets that carved out deep U-shaped valleys, plucking away rocks and soil that lay in their path. As the glaciers advanced, the species that could not survive the harsh arctic conditions were forced to migrate southwards and eastwards into continental Europe where temperatures were higher. At this time sea-level was much lower than it is today, because so much water was bound up in the ice. Britain was not an island but joined to the continent and Ireland by landbridges. It is thought that some species may have survived in Britain during glaciation by retreating to ice-free sheltered refuges, similar to the nunataks among the arctic ice. Such refuges may have included Breadalbane in Scotland, Teesdale in northern England and Cwm Idwal in Snowdonia.

During glaciation the British landscape may have resembled Spitsbergen in the Arctic.

H. S. Pardoe

As the climate improved following glaciation and the glaciers retreated, large areas of bare glacial deposits were left. The ground would have been extremely cold, unstable and subject to both waterlogging and desiccation (depending on temperature conditions and the rate of melting). The substrate consisted mainly of large angular boulders, with much of the finer material and nutrients being quickly washed away by the glacier melt-water or removed by wind. Initially there would have been very little soil and what there was would have been alkaline. However, the specially-adapted arctic-alpine plants were well placed to exploit the situation. These pioneer species, advancing from their refuges and migrating back from the continent, quickly colonised the bare ground. It is thought that some species may have reached Europe via a landbridge from Greenland and North America in the west. The vegetation in Britain at this time probably resembled the present vegetation in the Arctic, consisting of small patches of mosses, lichens, herbs and grasses.

As the climate improved further, other species, including shrubs and trees, better adapted to the warmer conditions, migrated back from the south. The arctic-alpine plants were unable to compete; often they were shaded out or could not tolerate the high summer temperatures. They were forced to retreat to higher altitudes where the woody plants could not survive. This produced small isolated populations with impoverished gene pools. Possibly, during the warmest phase, when treelines were higher than they are now, some arctic-alpine plants became extinct. As the icesheets melted the sea-level rose and the landbridges were submerged. The re-establishment of the English Channel and the Irish Sea meant that further migration from the continent was halted. The relatively impoverished flora of the British Isles, compared to adjacent parts of Europe, suggests that many species were not able to migrate back quickly enough.

The arctic-alpine plants of the British Isles are now confined to montane habitats where they must survive low temperatures, strong winds, unstable soil conditions and very short growing seasons. Their existence is also under constant threat from grazing animals and human disturbance. The mountains provide a variety of habitats including mobile screes, exposed rock faces and wet, mossy flushes. The richest sites, botanically, are moist north-facing cliffs and inaccessible rock ledges, particularly those flushed with a constant supply of nutrient-rich moisture. Indeed, the combination of steep cliffs, harsh climate and soil instability provides the most suitable environment for mountain plants because their adaptations allow them to survive where more demanding plants cannot.

Arctic-alpine plants continue to respond to climatic changes, whether natural or man-induced. For example, there is evidence that global warming is causing the icesheets to recede in the Antarctic. The species growing at the ice margins are able to colonise the freshly exposed land and to reproduce more successfully, leading to more individuals and an increase in their range.

Adaptations

Arctic-alpine plants exhibit several adaptations that allow them to survive the harsh environment in which they live. Perhaps the main limiting factors are the low temperatures, temperature extremes, prevalence of strong winds and the very short growing season. The majority of mountain plants are very small, have creeping stems or are prostrate which means that they can live in the layer of relatively warm still air at the ground surface. Exposure is further reduced by their habit of growing in hollows between boulders, or in crevices on rock faces. The low growth form also allows them to retain an insulating covering of snow through the winter and reduces the impact of high levels of ultraviolet radiation. Many mountain plants form cushions, mats or tufts so that each individual plant is protected by those around it and overall evaporation is reduced.

Despite the prevalence of high rainfall in mountain areas, there are still long dry periods and the frequency of strong winds contributes to desiccation problems. Adaptations to reduce water-loss include small leaves, hairy leaves or leaves that are covered with a thick waxy cuticle. Often arctic-alpine plants have a stout taproot that provides a strong anchorage and allows them access to nutrients deep in the soil. This is particularly important where the soil is disturbed by frost heaving, leaching and mass movement, so that mature soils cannot develop.

The reproductive cycle is often very short, an adaptation to exploit the brief summer, when conditions are favourable. In parts of the Arctic, such as Spitsbergen, the plants may have only six weeks to produce stems, leaves and flowers and for the seeds to ripen. Often arctic plants will flower only a few days after being uncovered by snow. The reproductive cycle may span several years; the buds being produced the year before the flowers actually open. Alternatively, several species reproduce vegetatively, for example, by producing plantlets or bulbils rather than flowers.

History

One of the greatest threats to arctic-alpine plants is collecting. The Victorians in particular were enthusiastic collectors of rare plants, especially ferns, that were often pressed and kept in private herbaria. At the height of this fashion, guides in Snowdonia openly sold rare plants on the mountain summits. Botanists were employed to find specific plants and there are reports that one of the most famous, Samuel Brewer, removed a rare *Woodsia alpina* from an inaccessible ledge using a twenty foot pole. A consequence of this craze for collecting was that the populations of many rare species were seriously depleted. Many species have declined in frequency due to a combination of over-collection, isolation of populations, a limited gene pool, the impact of grazing and the fact that many of the species are already at the extremes of their ecological range. Technical developments have now made it possible to identify plants from photographs rather than from pressed specimens and the discovery of a rarity can now be recorded without damaging the plant.

The medicinal properties of many mountain plants have long been recognised and have attracted many collectors. For example, the saxifrages that often grow on bare rock beside mountain streams were prescribed by herbalists such as Culpeper to cleanse the urine and break kidney stones. The bitter-tasting chemicals stored in the leaves of mountain gentians have been used to treat fevers and anaemia.

Cultivated alpine plants have become increasingly popular with gardeners. The Alpine Garden Society is a valuable source of information and seeds for

Many rare British mountain plants are more widespread in alpine regions such as the Jotunheim Mountains in Norway.

H. S. Pardoe

enthusiasts. Garden centres sell acclimatised stock of many of the most attractive species that will grow successfully on rockeries.

Conservation and legal protection

The isolated populations of arctic-alpine plants are very vulnerable to any form of human disturbance. It is not unknown for climbers to strip away plants in an effort to find an elusive fingerhold. Increasing numbers of visitors to the mountains represent a threat to arctic-alpine plants. This presents conservation bodies with a dilemma since it is understandable that people wish to have unrestricted access to the mountains and to be able to explore and discover these beautiful mountain plants. However, this must be balanced against the need to protect rare plants; one careless action can destroy a plant that has been struggling to grow for decades. A degree of secrecy surrounds the exact location of several of the rarest plants; this is essential to deter collectors. Particularly worrying are plans for new large-scale ski developments that have the potential to cause widespread damage in these extremely fragile and sensitive environments.

Conservationists have in some cases taken action to prevent a species becoming locally extinct; to manage the local environment in such a way as to protect the arctic-alpine species; or to provide suitable conditions for them to extend their range. This can involve restocking (where the species still occurs at the site) or reintroduction (where the species is thought to have once grown but has died out). For example, the Ben Lawers National Nature Reserve in Tayside is probably the best site for arctic-alpine species in Britain, boasting 60% of the British mountain flora. The combination of rich calcareous microschists, unstable, high altitude mountains and relatively harsh but stable climate provides ideal conditions. Strenuous efforts are being made to protect this unique flora. Detailed surveys are conducted to monitor the populations and distribution of the rarest species. Several exclosures exist where the vegetation is protected from grazing by the large populations of sheep and deer. Species such as shrub willows, which are now largely confined to inaccessible cliffs by intensive grazing, have been planted in environments where only a few individual plants survived, to recreate habitats such as streamside willow thickets that are thought to have existed here in the past.

Similarly, in the mid 1970s Tufted Saxifrage (*Saxifraga cespitosa*) was identified as an endangered species in north Wales by the Nature Conservancy Council. This population (the only one in Britain outside the Scottish Highlands) had been reduced by collecting to four plants on a single mountain ledge. Seeds were gathered from the remaining plants and seedlings were cultivated at the University of Liverpool Botanic Gardens. 420 plants and 1,500 seeds were planted at sites in Cwm Idwal where they were thought to have grown formerly. After 15 years there is now a stable population of some 50 plants.

These two commendable programmes demonstrate that the deleterious impact of Man can be reduced by suitable management programmes. These often require detailed knowledge of the ecological requirements of the species and long-term monitoring programmes are needed to assess the success of the programme. Obviously such programmes need to be designed

Cwm Idwal in the Snowdonia National Park

carefully to be sensitive to the plant community involved. Where there has been substantial and prolonged human activity it can be difficult to determine the nature and species composition of the 'natural' vegetation. However, this can be largely assessed by reference to historical records, palaeobotanical evidence such as pollen and plant remains preserved in peat or by comparison with present-day arctic-alpine environments.

Numerous bodies are involved in the conservation of arctic-alpine plants. These include government bodies such as the Countryside Council for Wales, Scottish Natural Heritage, English Nature, the National Parks Authorities, as well as various voluntary organisations such as the National Trust and local conservation trusts. Many of the rarest plants are found in National Nature Reserves and Sites of Special Scientific Interest which affords them additional protection. Several laws exist to protect the rare plants described in this book including the Wildlife and Countryside Act (1981) that makes it illegal to uproot any wild plant without the landowner's permission. Many endangered species, listed in the British Red Data book, are given additional protection by the Wildlife and Countryside Act (1981). Under this act it is an offence to pick, remove or destroy any part (including seeds) of the species listed in Schedule 8, or to attempt to do so, or to trade in these species.

In a book of this size it has not been possible to produce a comprehensive survey of the British arctic-alpine flora. Regrettably, several beautiful species such as the Drooping Saxifrage (*Saxifraga cernua*), Cyphel (*Minuartia sedoides*) and Alpine Forget-me-not (*Myosotis alpestris*), have been omitted. Many species such as Moschatel (*Adoxa moschatellina*), Welsh Poppy (*Meconopsis cambrica*), Common Butterwort (*Pinguicula vulgaris*), Harebell (*Campanula rotundifolia*) and Globeflower (*Trollius europaeus*) that are frequently found growing in the mountains, have been excluded because they are more common in lowland habitats. The selection has been a personal choice, made with the aim of including a representative selection. The plants described are arranged in alphabetical order of their Latin name. A variety of sources has been used during the preparation of the text and maps presented in this book. Where species have broad distributions and variable ecological requirements, characteristics such as height or flowering period will vary according to local environmental conditions. For consistency the flowering period listed in Clapham, Tutin, and Moore (1987) has been quoted. The nomenclature follows Stace (1991). The maps are intended as a guide to the distribution and relative frequency of the individual species. The black shading indicates the main area of distribution and the grey shading indicates where the plant has a scattered distribution or where it is comparatively rare.

It is hoped that this book will promote the understanding and enjoyment of arctic-alpine plants and that it will encourage people to treat them with the care and respect they deserve.

Alpine Lady's-mantle *Alchemilla alpina*

Alpine Lady's-mantle grows up to 20 cm tall. It has a woody, creeping stock. The palmate leaves are divided into 5 to 7 separate leaflets that are white and silky beneath and sharply toothed at the tip. Often the brown remnants of the previous year's leaves can be seen at the base of the plant. The delicate, tiny, yellowish-green flowers form a dense cluster. They open between June and August.

This species grows on mountain tops and early exposed snowbeds, in mountain pastures, rock crevices and screes, preferring acid soils. The range of Alpine Lady's-mantle in the British Isles includes the Lake District, northern England and central and northern Scotland, although it is very rare in Ireland. Its altitudinal range is from sea-level on Skye to over 1215 m in the Cairngorms. It is also found in Greenland and in north, west and central Europe, including the eastern Alps and the Apennines.

D. K. Mardon

Mountain Everlasting *Antennaria dioica*

Mountain Everlasting has creeping stolons and erect woolly flowering shoots that grow up to 20 cm tall. It has characteristic blue-green woolly leaves that form a basal rosette. The stem leaves are spoon shaped and arranged in spirals. There are separate male and female plants; the male plant is the smaller. The flowering period is June to July, the flowering heads consisting of a cluster of 2 to 8 flowers. The bracts can be pink, red or white and they look rather like the paws of a cat, giving rise to an alternative name for this species – Cat's foot.

This species grows on heaths, moors, mountain slopes and dry pastures, usually over limestone or basic igneous rock. It is found in northern Britain, Wales and western Ireland (to 1000 m in Scotland). Its range also includes northern and central Europe, Siberia, western Asia and North America.

D. K. Mardon

11

Alpine Rock-cress *Arabis alpina*

Alpine Rock-cress is a perennial plant that forms mats or loose tufts. It is generally 6 – 40 cm tall. It has toothed hairy leaves; the stem leaves are stalkless, their base clasping the stem. The flowers are white and form dense clusters. They open between June and August.

This species prefers limestone and north-facing slopes and is found in damp rocky places, stream sides, flushed snowbeds, ledges, gravel and steppe. It was first discovered in Britain as recently as 1887 and is still known from only two rock-ledges in the Black Cuillins in Skye at approximately 840 m. For this reason it is listed on Schedule 8 of the Wildlife and Countryside Act (1981). This is a widespread arctic-alpine plant of the northern hemisphere; its range includes Europe, Greenland, arctic north-east Canada and arctic Siberia. Its most northerly location is at a latitude of 79° 35' N in Spitsbergen.

D. K. Mardon

12

Northern Rock-cress *Arabis petraea*

This species is a perennial herb with stout tap root and basal rosette of leaves. It forms mats and is usually 10 – 25 cm tall. Its white or purplish flowers open between June and August. It is usually self-pollinated and grows on scree slopes, gravel bars, stream beds, rock crevices and ledges. Northern Rock-cress is often a pioneer plant that grows on moraines, roadsides and in gravel pits. It is occasionally found near the coast.

This species prefers calcareous rocks. Its range includes north Wales, Scotland and also Ireland where it occurs locally. In Scotland it has an altitudinal range from sea-level to over 1200 m. It is also found in the mountains of central Europe and in the Faeroes, Iceland, Scandinavia, Finland, Siberia and North America.

H. S. Pardoe

Alpine Bartsia *Bartsia alpina*

Alpine Bartsia is a perennial plant, covered in soft white hairs. It has an underground creeping rhizome with several upright stems, that reach up to 10 – 30 cm tall. Its purple flowers open between June and August. They are arranged in short spikes among large purplish leafy bracts. The oval toothed leaves grow in opposite pairs. It has large, winged seeds. This species is semi-parasitic, usually growing on grasses. Linnaeus named this plant after his friend Johann Bartsch who died while researching the tropical flora of South America.

Alpine Bartsia grows in mountain pastures, damp meadows, fens, willow thickets, birch forests, snowbeds and rock ledges, preferring basic damp soils. It is confined to mountains in northern Britain (from Yorkshire to Perthshire) at altitudes up to 1000 m. Elsewhere in its range (that includes northern Europe, the Pyrenees, Greenland and North America) it occurs at altitudes between 1100 m and 2700 m.

D. Parish

14

Alpine Mouse-ear *Cerastium alpinum*

Alpine Mouse-ear is a greyish-green plant, with pubescent stems and leaves. It grows up to 20 cm tall and forms mats or tufts. Its white flowers have notched petals. The flowers open between June and August.

Its range includes north Wales, northern England and Scotland. Meadows, heaths and ledges are typical habitats of this species. It prefers well-drained soils over calcareous rocks and reaches an altitude of 1213 m on Ben Lawers. This plant has been recorded from 83°24'N in northern Greenland; according to Clapham, Tutin and Warburg (1952) this is the 'northernmost botanical locality on earth'. It also grows in northern Europe, Iceland, Jan Mayen, and in the mountains of central and south-west Europe and eastern North America.

D. K. Mardon

15

Parsley Fern *Cryptogramma crispa*

Parsley Fern grows in dense tufts usually between 15 – 25 cm in height. It is a small fern with separate vegetative and spore producing fronds. The fertile fronds have linear segments while the sterile fronds are broader and toothed. The vivid light-green fronds emerge in late-May to mid-June and the spores are shed through July and August. It is thought to be poisonous, especially to horses.

It is an oceanic species that needs a moist climate throughout the year. It cannot tolerate severe winter cold or high maximum summer temperatures. The latter determines the limit of its southward range in Britain. At high altitude it is confined to sites where a thick blanket of winter snow provides protection against cold and winter desiccation. It prefers sites with free-drainage and can grow on relatively mobile scree, acting as a pioneer. It is frequently found on sandstones, gritstones, shales and slates, preferring siliceous, acid soils. Parsley Fern is frequently found in corrie sites in the mountains of north Wales, the Lake District and the Scottish Southern Uplands at altitudes of 100 – 1220 m. It is also found in high mountains of Europe, especially in Scandinavia. Related forms occur discontinuously in the Himalayas and far east of Asia and in northern and western North America.

D. K. Mardon

16

Tufted Hair-grass *Deschampsia cespitosa* **ssp.** *alpina*

Tufted Hair-grass is usually 10 – 40 cm tall. The leaves are short and hooded at
the apex. It grows in tufts at high altitude (900 – 1350 m), preferring moist
rocks, sands and gravels, flushed snowbeds, and grassy slopes. The flowering
period is between June and August. It is viviparous, with the young plants
being produced on the parent plant, rather than from seeds.

It is most frequent in the western and central Highlands and occurs locally
in parts of north Wales, north-west England and Ireland. This species is also
found in Scandinavia, Iceland, Greenland, arctic Russia and Siberia.

H. S. Pardoe

17

Diapensia *Diapensia lapponica*

Diapensia is a small cushion-like or creeping undershrub that is usually only 2 – 6 cm tall. It has a stout taproot and woody stems. The evergreen, leathery leaves are arranged in rosettes. Its pale yellow flowers open between May and June.

Diapensia grows on the most exposed ridges that are very dry in summer and sparsely covered by snow in winter. It is also found in gravelly, rocky places and on heaths. This species is very rare in Britain and was first discovered in 1951. It has been recorded at only two sites on exposed ridges at 760 m and 850 m in West Inverness. Consequently there is stringent legal protection; it is one of the species listed on Schedule 8 of the Wildlife and Countryside Act (1981).

On the broader scale, it is a circumpolar arctic species, that avoids high arctic areas. It occurs as far south as 60°N in Norway and extends to the Urals and to New York. The remains of Diapensia in late-glacial deposits indicate that it survived in the North Atlantic area during the last major glaciation.

D. K. Mardon

Alpine Clubmoss *Diphasiastrum alpinum*

A common sight at high altitude is the Alpine Clubmoss. This is a relatively simple plant, related to the ferns, that has stems that are frequently branched. Its creeping form is often seen growing over exposed rockfaces. The leaves of this plant are small and scale-like to reduce water loss.

The most common habitats of Alpine Clubmoss are moors, grassland and mountain tops, where it reaches altitudes up to 1220 m. In the British Isles it is found in north and mid Wales, northern England, north and west Ireland and throughout Scotland. Alpine Clubmoss also grows in northern and central Europe, Asia Minor, the Caucasus, North America and Japan.

P. Russell

19

Hoary Whitlowgrass *Draba incana*

Hoary Whitlowgrass is a tufted perennial with leafy, many-flowered, erect stems that are generally 5 – 50 cm tall. It has a rosette of coarsely toothed leaves. The white flowers open between June and July.

It grows on mountain rocks and is also found locally on screes, rock-ledges, and shelly sand dunes, preferring calcareous soils on limestone. Hoary Whitlowgrass occurs in the British Isles mainly north of Derbyshire. Isolated populations are also found in western Ireland and north Wales. Its altitudinal range is from sea level to 1080 m on Ben Lawers. On the broader scale, this species is found in central Europe, central Asia, arctic and subarctic Europe, Iceland and Greenland.

D. K. Mardon

Mountain Avens *Dryas octopetala*

Mountain Avens is an evergreen, prostrate dwarf shrub forming tufts or large mats. It has woody stems and a tough rootstock. Its oval leaves are dark glossy green and glabrous above and densely white tomentose beneath, with roundly-toothed edges. The flower stalks are 3 – 10 cm tall. Its Latin name is derived from the eight petals that form the creamy white flower. The persistent style, with its white feathery hairs, is important to the dispersal of the seeds by wind. The flowering period is from June until July.

Mountain Avens grows in dry localities where snow melts early, in the mountains on ledges and in crevices, on gravel, scree slopes, sea cliffs and rocky barrens, often forming a distinct species-rich heath community. This species is a very good indicator of calcareous base-rich soils. In the British Isles it is most frequent in western Ireland (particularly the Burren) and north and west Scotland but it is also found locally in north Wales, northern Ireland and northern England. It occurs at altitudes from almost sea-level in north-west Scotland and western Ireland to 1050 m.

This species has broad ecological requirements that perhaps explain its broad distribution, ranging from arctic, subarctic and central Europe, to Asia and the Rocky Mountains in North America. During the last glaciation, *Dryas* grew in the environs of the Scandinavian icesheet. Abundant fossil remains of this plant have been found in southern England and lowland Europe and these have given rise to the names Older Dryas and Younger Dryas for two of the cold phases during the late-glacial.

D. K. Mardon

21

Viviparous Sheep's-fescue *Festuca vivipara*

Viviparous Sheep's-fescue is a tufted perennial grass that grows up to 40 cm tall. It has hair-like leaves that are inrolled. The flowers open between June and August. As its name suggests, it is a viviparous species; young plants develop on the spikelets.

It grows on mountain rocks and in grassy places, extending to sea-level in north and west Scotland. Its range extends from mid Wales to Scotland and Ireland in the British Isles and also encompasses the Arctic and north-east Europe.

D. K. Mardon

22

Alpine Gentian *Gentiana nivalis*

Alpine Gentian is a small annual that grows up to 15 cm tall. The slender, erect, branching stems of this plant give it a fragile appearance. The attractive small starry flowers are usually a brilliant deep blue but may occasionally be white, and open between July and September. They are very sensitive to temperature changes – the petals close spirally when the temperature goes below 10°C. As a result, this species often goes unnoticed at lower temperatures.

This is a rare plant in Britain, listed on Schedule 8 of the Wildlife and Countryside Act (1981). It is confined to mountain rock ledges in Perth and Angus (above 730 m). In contrast, it is relatively common in many parts of northern Europe, such as Norway where it grows on gravels, rock ledges and river banks. It is found in grassland, meadows, heaths and birch forests. Alpine Gentian is also found in central and southern Europe (including the Pyrenees and southern Apennines), Asia Minor, the Caucasus, Greenland and arctic North America.

D. K. Mardon

Spring Gentian *Gentiana verna*

Spring Gentian is a perennial plant that grows up to 7 cm tall. The flowers are solitary and open between April and June. They are usually a brilliant deep blue but they can occasionally be white, pale blue, pinkish or reddish purple, often with a white throat. At high altitude, the flowers open as the snow recedes. The lance-shaped leaves are arranged in rosettes.

This is a very local plant of grassy places on limestone in northern England (up to 800 m) and in Clare, Galway and Mayo in western Ireland. It also grows on calcareous glacial drift and fixed dunes. Like the Alpine Gentian, this species is listed on Schedule 8 of the Wildlife and Countryside Act (1981). Beyond the British Isles, it is found in central and southern Europe, arctic Russia, the Caucasus, Morocco and parts of Asia.

D. Parish

Dwarf Cudweed *Gnaphalium supinum*

Dwarf Cudweed is a perennial plant that grows in tufts. It has creeping stems that range in height from 2 to 12 cm. The narrow lance-shaped leaves are woolly on both sides. The flowers usually open in July and consist of a cluster of between one and seven heads. Each head is surrounded by dark brown bracts.

Dwarf Cudweed grows in damp meadows, late-exposed snowbeds, mountain rocks and gravel, moraines and cliffs. It prefers acid soils. This species is extremely rare in Britain, where it is confined to the Scottish mountains in Skye and from Stirling to Sutherland on the mainland. It is more widespread in the mountains of central Europe, western Asia, arctic Europe, Greenland and North America.

D. K. Mardon

Alpine Hawkweed *Hieracium* sect. *Alpina*

The taxonomy of this genus is extremely complex, since thousands of microspecies have been described. One group of this genus frequently found in the British uplands is the Alpine Hawkweed group (*Hieracium* sect. *Alpina*) which consists of 18 microspecies. These are generally 10 – 20 cm tall with deep-green basal leaves that are often toothed and with a single small stem-leaf. The stem, leaves and bracts are covered with hairs and small glands. The single, golden-yellow, flower heads open between July and August.

Alpine Hawkweed is most common on rock ledges, ridges and heaths, meadows and screes on acid soils. In Britain it is found in mainland Scotland, north Wales and the Lake District, usually above 650 m. It also grows in the mountains of central and northern Europe. The name *Hieracium* is derived from the Greek for hawk because it was thought that this sharp-eyed bird extracted the plant's juices to strengthen its sight.

H. Angel, Biofotos.

26

Iceland-purslane *Koenigia islandica*

Iceland-purslane is a tiny annual that is usually less than 7 cm tall. It has smooth, fleshy leaves that are sometimes opposite. The clustered small yellowish-green flowers are quite inconspicuous, and appear between June and August.

This plant usually grows in wet, open localities (where there is little competition) such as base-rich soils, fens, cold springs, stony and gravelly ground and late-melting snowbeds. It has a circumpolar arctic distribution including the Faeroes, Iceland, Jan Mayen and Svalbard as well as mountains of central Asia and Tierra del Fuego at the southern tip of South America. It does not grow in central Europe, although late-glacial and post-glacial fossils have been found there, and also in southernmost Norway, southern Sweden and Scotland. In Norway this species is found near upland, summer farms, in ditches and places where trampling cattle create open muddy patches.

In Britain Iceland-purslane was first discovered in 1934, on the summit of the Storr in Skye. However, it was mistakenly labelled *Peplis portula*, before being sent to the Herbarium at Kew. The mistake went undetected until 1950 when the find was finally published. Subsequent investigation revealed that it is relatively frequent in the Storr range, where it is thought to be a glacial relict. It is restricted to Skye and Mull in western Scotland, above 460 m.

L. Farrell

27

Snowdon Lily *Lloydia serotina*

The first discovery of the Snowdon Lily in Britain was by Edward Lhwyd. His find was published by John Ray in the *Synopsis Methodica Stirpium Britannicarum* (Synopsis of British Plants) in 1696. This species is a bulbous perennial; this adaptation allows it to survive periods of extreme cold when dormant. It is short, growing to a maximum height of 15 cm, and produces delicate pale cream flowers, sometimes having pink streaks, that open in June. The Snowdon Lily is thought to be a glacial relict in Britain, being found only on inaccessible rocky ledges and in cracks at high altitude (460 – 760 m) in the Snowdon range.

This small colony is 1050 km from its nearest neighbours in the Alps and 7500 km from those in North America. It is confined to five sites in north- and east- facing cirques where the snow cover is shallow and infrequent, and it prefers locations that are exposed to the wind, sheltered from direct sunlight and frequently enveloped in mist. One observer (J.E.Griffith) saw basketsfull being carried away in the 1880s. Today it is a protected species on Schedule 8 of the Wildlife and Countryside Act (1981) and must not be picked.

Its range extends beyond Britain to arctic Russia, the Alps, the Carpathians, Soviet Asia, Japan, the Himalayas, China, western North America and New Mexico.

D. Parish

Alpine Catchfly *Lychnis alpina*

Alpine Catchfly generally grows in dense tufts between 5 and 20 cm in height. The flowering period is June to July. It has characteristic small, deep reddish pink flowers, that are clustered in a dense head. The petals are bifid or notched. The spear-shaped leaves usually form a rosette.

This species grows on exposed alpine moors, meadows, stony places, gravel, Mountain Avens heaths, cliff ledges, scree slopes and shallow rich fens, usually on siliceous rocks but also acid soils. It often occurs on substrates containing heavy metals (such as copper, zinc and nickel) and also serpentine and slag heaps. This is a subarctic-alpine species, with its stronghold in Fennoscandia. It also occurs in the Alps, the Pyrenees, western Asia, North America and Greenland (where it reaches a latitude of 73°10'N). This is another very rare species in Britain, found only in the Lake District and in the Clova Mountains of Scotland, at altitudes up to 900 m. It is listed on Schedule 8 of the Wildlife and Countryside Act (1981).

It is thought to be a glacial relict at coastal sites in Norway and Sweden. It was widely distributed during early postglacial times, but was ousted by competitors except in specialised habitats such as coastal cliffs.

D. K. Mardon

Mountain Sandwort *Minuartia rubella*

The stems of the Mountain Sandwort form dense tufts that are usually 2 – 8 cm in height. It has small linear leaves. The delicate flowers open between June and August. The petals of this plant are white or sometimes pink.

It is found on ledges, heaths, screes, rocks and dry gravel on calcareous soils, reaching altitudes up to 1158 m. Exposed habitats are preferred, including gravelly patches eroded by the wind. This is a circumpolar arctic species that is relatively rare in northern Scotland and the Faeroes but common in Iceland, Norway, Siberia, Greenland and North America.

D. K. Mardon

Spring Sandwort *Minuartia verna*

Spring Sandwort has linear leaves and leafy shoots that form tufts or cushions that are anchored by a stout taproot. It grows up to 15 cm tall. The white flowers open between May and September. It prefers rocky places, screes and sparse grassland, often on lead-mine spoil. For this reason it is called Leadwort in the Peak District.

Spring Sandwort is locally abundant on upland calcareous and limestone rocks and moors in northern England, Wales and western Ireland. It is rare in Scotland, south-west England and northern Ireland. The distribution of this species is rather unusual; it grows in central and continental Europe, Siberia, the Caucasus and north Africa but is absent from Scandinavia and the Baltic.

D. K. Mardon

Mountain Sorrel *Oxyria digyna*

Mountain Sorrel forms dense tufts of kidney-shaped leaves. The erect stems are usually 5 – 30 cm high. The flowering stems emerge from the tufts in open upright clusters. The flowers, which open between July and August, are small, green and later reddish.

This species grows in the mountains in wet places, flushed snowbeds, springs, rocky ledges, screes, ravines and river-bars, often in abundance. It occurs on both acid and base-rich soils, preferring sites that are protected by snow in winter. It is a pioneer plant that grows on ground recently uncovered by ice. Late-glacial fossil finds in Denmark show that it apparently grew near the ice margin during the last glaciation.

The name *Oxyria* is derived from the Greek word for sour. The edible leaves have a fresh acidic taste, and are rich in Vitamin C. In the Arctic it has been used to prevent and cure scurvy and has also been used by Lapps to turn reindeer milk sour. It has a broad distribution including Scandinavia, central Europe, central Asia and the Rocky Mountains. In Britain it is found mainly in north Wales, north-west England and Scotland.

D. K. Mardon

32

Alpine Bistort *Persicaria vivipara*

Alpine Bistort is usually 5 – 30 cm tall. It is a slender erect plant with a thick rootstock. The leaves are long and narrow with thick cross-veins. The flowers are white or pink in the upper part of the spike; lower ones are replaced by dark purple bulbils. The flowering period is usually between June and August. At high altitude or latitude the flowers rarely produce viable seed and the plant normally reproduces by the bulbils. These are rich in starch which makes them a preferred food for ptarmigan and reindeer. In times of famine it has occasionally been eaten by arctic people.

This species prefers calcareous soils. It is relatively common in grassland and on rock-ledges in mountain districts of Scotland and northern England but it is very rare in north Wales and south-west Ireland. In Scotland it has an altitudinal range from sea-level to 1350 m. It also grows in the mountains of northern Europe, central and southern Asia and North America.

D. K. Mardon

33

Alpine Meadow-grass *Poa alpina*

Alpine Meadow-grass is a tufted perennial plant and can be up to 40 cm tall. It has broad, blunt, boat-shaped leaves and large spikelets. There are generally 2 – 5 flowers on each spikelet, that open between July and August. A characteristic feature is the presence of light-coloured, persistent, fibrous remains of basal leaves and sheaths. At high altitudes it reproduces asexually by developing young plantlets in the spikelets instead of flowers. These are dispersed by wind or water. In Britain this species rarely produces seeds.

This plant is found in sites with a long-lasting snow cover, preferring base-rich soils. In the British Isles it is a rare grass of gullies, rocky and stony places on the upper slopes of the mountains of north Wales, the Lake District, the Scottish Highlands and southern Ireland; from 300 to 1220 m. It also occurs throughout the Arctic and at high elevations in temperate Europe, north Africa, Asia and North America.

D. K. Mardon

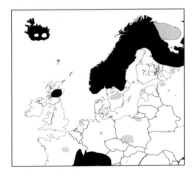

34

Holly-fern *Polystichum lonchitis*

Holly-fern has a short stout rhizome. The fronds are usually 15 – 30 cm long, and the margins bear long colourless spines which are responsible for the English name. The fronds are divided into 20 – 40 pairs of oval leaflets with toothed edges. The new fronds begin to grow in mid-May, and are fertile, producing sooty-black spores until the following April.

Holly-fern is found in mountainous areas, often in crevices and rock gullies and on screes above the tree-line. It prefers base-rich soils and has a discontinuous range around the northern hemisphere. It is particularly widespread in an arctic-alpine pattern through the central European mountains (and especially the Alps), western Scandinavia and Iceland, the Caucasus and Himalaya. In the British Isles, this species is generally confined to central and north-west Scotland, with a few local and generally disjunct stations, mainly in northern England, north-west Wales and in the extreme west of Ireland. It is generally found above 600 m, occasionally reaching altitudes of 1070 m.

D. K. Mardon

Alpine Cinquefoil *Potentilla crantzii*

Alpine Cinquefoil grows up to 25 cm tall. It has characteristic palmate leaves consisting of 3 to 5 leaflets, arranged in terminal rosettes. The flowers are golden yellow, sometimes with an orange spot at the base of the petals. They open in June and July.

This species grows on basic mountain rock ledges, gravel, heaths and scree slopes, in crevices, grassland and meadows. In Britain it is found locally in north Wales, northern England and Scotland but is absent from Ireland. In regions such as the Pyrenees and the Alps it is found at altitudes up to 3000 m. Its broad range encompasses northern Europe, the mountains of central and southern Europe, northern Asia, North America, the Caucasus, Asia Minor and Iran.

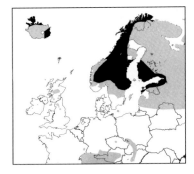

Dwarf Willow *Salix herbacea*

Dwarf Willow produces underground branches which grow from a long, creeping rhizome. The aerial branches of this shrub are very short and often prostrate. The green, glossy leaves, with serrated edges, usually rest on the ground. Dwarf Willow flowers between June and July.

Common habitats of this plant include rock ledges and rocky mountain-tops, late exposed snowbeds, damp meadows and heath communities. It often forms dense carpets and is locally common in Scotland, northern England and parts of Wales and Ireland, reaching altitudes of 1300 m. It is also found in arctic Eurasia, the Pyrenees, the Alps, the Apennines and Norway where it reaches altitudes up to 2170 m.

D. K. Mardon

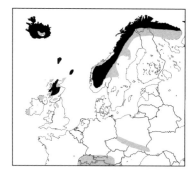

37

Alpine Saw-wort *Saussurea alpina*

Alpine Saw-wort is a perennial herb, with short erect stems that are usually 10 – 45 cm tall. The stem and underside of the toothed leaves are covered in white-cottony hairs. This plant has blue or purplish, vanilla-scented flowers that form dense clusters. The flowering period is August to September.

In Scandinavia this species is found in birch forests, willow thickets, screes, fens, meadows and heaths, and is abundant in snowbeds, stony places and ridges, preferring calcareous soils. It occurs in the central and eastern Pyrenees, the Alps and Norway at altitudes of 1500 – 3000 m. It is thought to be a postglacial relict in southern Sweden. Closely related species occur in Siberia and the arctic, extending to a latitude of 75°N. Its range in the British Isles extends from Scotland to north Wales and Ireland (to 1300 m) on mountain cliffs and scree. It is also found at coastal locations in northern Scotland.

D. K. Mardon

Yellow Saxifrage *Saxifraga aizoides*

Yellow Saxifrage has a creeping-lifeform and often forms mats or tufts. It normally grows to 5 – 25 cm in height. Despite a preference for moist localities it has fleshy sessile leaves that are adapted to reduce water loss. The flowering stems are branched, bearing a group of 5 – 10 starry flowers which open between June and August. The petals of this species are usually yellow with orange spots matching the colour of the anthers, but occasionally it has orange petals with red spots and anthers.

This plant grows mainly in moist places, including wet rocks, gravel near streams, stony ground and on irrigated slopes and cliffs, preferring base-rich soils. In the British Isles Yellow Saxifrage has a local distribution in northern England, Scotland and Ireland, reaching altitudes up to 1175 m and descending to sea-level on dunes in northern Scotland. Although now extinct in Wales, it grew there as recently as 1900. This species has a broad range outside the British Isles, including arctic and subarctic Europe, Greenland, North America, western Asia, as well as the high mountains of northern and central Europe, from the Pyrenees to the Carpathians.

D. K. Mardon

Tufted Saxifrage *Saxifraga cespitosa*

The perennial Tufted Saxifrage is usually 5 – 12 cm tall, and as the name implies, forms dense cushions, each with a stout taproot. Its attractive white or yellow flowers most frequently open between May and July. The leaves, stems and sepals are covered in glandular hairs. The leaves are divided into 3 – 5 lobes and form a basal rosette.

This species grows in dry places, preferably on base-rich soils, ledges, gravel, Mountain Avens heaths, exposed ridges by cairns and on mountain tops manured by birds. In Britain it is rare, being mainly found locally in mountains in central Scotland and north Wales above 600 m. For this reason it is listed on Schedule 8 of the Wildlife and Countryside Act (1981). It is more widespread in arctic and subarctic Europe, Asia and America.

H. S. Pardoe

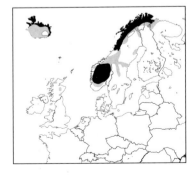

Mossy Saxifrage *Saxifraga hypnoides*

Mossy Saxifrage forms mats of radiating leafy shoots. It is generally 5 – 30 cm tall. The flowering stems bear 3 to 7 white flowers, in a small head, that open between May and July.

This plant grows mainly in mountainous areas on rock ledges, boulders, screes, streamsides, stony grassy places and dunes on wet, base rich substrata to 1300 m. In the British Isles it is found locally as far south as north Somerset. It occurs through much of north-west Europe, southwards to the Vosges.

D. K. Mardon

41

Alpine Saxifrage *Saxifraga nivalis*

Alpine Saxifrage is relatively rare in Britain. It has a stout pubescent stem that grows up to 20 cm tall. It has thick toothed rounded leathery leaves (often reddish beneath), arranged in a basal rosette. The clustered greenish-white or pink flowers open between July and August.

This species grows on dry rocky slopes, gravel, crevices and ledges, preferring wet, base-rich soils. It is mainly restricted to the Scottish mountains, but also occurs locally in north Wales, north-west Ireland and north-west England. Its range extends to arctic and subarctic Europe, Asia, North America, Greenland and the Sudetan Mountains.

D. Parish

Purple Saxifrage *Saxifraga oppositifolia*

This saxifrage has long prostrate creeping stems and short erect woody branches. It grows in mats or tufts, often trailing over inaccessible boulders. Its small, rounded, scale-like, blue-green leaves often have lime encrusted tips. The Latin name is derived from the arrangement of leaves on opposite sides of the stem. It has a long flowering period, from March until July. The single, pink, purple or lilac flowers appear soon after the overlying snow has melted.

This species prefers calcareous soils, predominating on late-snowbeds. In the British Isles it is restricted to damp mountain rocks and scree in Scotland, north-west England and north and west Ireland. It is relatively rare in Wales, being found only in Snowdonia and the Brecon Beacons, and on Cader Idris. Its range extends to a latitude of 83°15'N in north Greenland, one of the most northerly-plant localities in the world. In the Arctic it extends over large areas, often colouring the landscape. It is found in the high mountains of arctic and subarctic Europe, Asia and America and reaches altitudes above 3000 m.

D. K. Mardon

Starry Saxifrage *Saxifraga stellaris*

Starry Saxifrage varies in height from 5 to 20 cm tall and flowers between June and August. The petals are white with two yellow or red spots near the base or are sometimes unspotted. The anthers are red or yellow. The toothed leaves are arranged in small rosettes at the base of the stem. This plant sometimes forms tufts. It grows in wet stony places, snowbeds, rock ledges, in flushes and by brooks, usually on acid soils.

Starry Saxifrage is relatively abundant in north Wales, northern England and Scotland but local in Ireland. It ascends to the top of Ben Nevis (1347 m). Its range in northern Europe extends from Iceland to arctic Russia and includes most major mountain ranges elsewhere in Europe, Greenland and Labrador.

D. K. Mardon

Roseroot *Sedum rosea*

Roseroot flowers between May and August. The stem is branched, thick and fleshy, growing up to 35 cm tall. The leaves are succulent and blue-green in colour. There are separate male and female plants. The yellow flowers form a dense head. Each female flower has 4 carpels that redden gradually. This plant generally has a stout taproot that provides a secure holdfast at exposed sites.

Roseroot prefers crevices, screes and inaccessible rock ledges on mountain rocks in Wales, Ireland, Scotland and northern England, ascending to 1175 m. It is also found on sea cliffs in western Scotland, Wales and Ireland. Its range includes arctic Europe, Asia and North America.

The stock has been used for food and for medicinal purposes and a decoction as a shampoo, which perhaps explains why its Norwegian name means 'growth of the hair'. It has often been planted on turf-covered roofs in the belief that it affords protection against lightning and fires.

D. K. Mardon

Sibbaldia *Sibbaldia procumbens*

Sibbaldia was named after Sir Robert Sibbald who published the first account of Scottish plants in 1684. It is a downy tufted perennial plant that is generally 3 – 10 cm tall. It has a woody stock and blueish-green leaves, that are often purplish below and usually arranged in a basal rosette. The leaves consist of three wedge-shaped lobes, each with a blunt end, bearing three teeth. The flower stems are often prostrate, with the inconspicuous flowers forming a dense cluster. The small, yellow petals are sometimes absent. The plant needs several years to mature before flowers develop. The flowering period is July – August.

Suitable habitats for this species include damp rocky places, mountain tops, screes, grasslands, willow thickets, meadows and grassy snowbeds, where it can be very abundant. In Britain it occurs from central Scotland northwards to Sutherland, at altitudes from 470 m to over 1340 m. It has been recorded in Westmorland but the reliability of this record has been questioned. This is the only species in this genus found in Europe; other, closely-related, species are restricted to the high mountains of Asia.

D. K. Mardon

46

Moss Campion *Silene acaulis*

Moss Campion is a perennial that grows in dense tufts. These form domed moss-like cushions composed of many long green shoots with much dead material underneath. Each cushion has a long taproot that penetrates deep into a rock crack. This species has narrow leaves, with short stiff hairs on the margin. In summer the surface of the cushion is covered by numerous pink (or occasionally white) flowers that have notched petals. The flowering season lasts from July to August. This long-lived species has male and female flowers on different plants.

Silene acaulis is found in arctic and alpine regions throughout Europe, east Siberia and North America, mainly on rock ledges, scree slopes and in dry gravelly places but also moist localities especially on mineral soil of calcareous rocks. It reaches a latitude of 83°N in Greenland. In Britain it is most frequent in north Wales, the Lake District and central and north-west Scotland, reaching altitudes up to 1250 m. It also occurs on cliffs, rocks and stabilised sand-dunes down to sea-level in the Hebrides, Orkney and Shetland.

D. K. Mardon

47

Alpine Meadow-rue *Thalictrum alpinum*

Alpine Meadow-rue is usually less than 15 cm tall. The apparently fragile stems are slender, wiry and glabrous, bearing leaves that are dark green above and whitish below. In June and July its clusters of pale yellow, drooping flowers appear.

This species grows best on wet mountain turf and rocks, Mountain Avens heaths, fens and ledges, on calcareous soils. In Britain it is found mainly in the north, from north Wales and Yorkshire. It also occurs in arctic and alpine Europe, Asia and North America.

D. K. Mardon

48

Scottish Asphodel *Tofieldia pusilla*

Scottish Asphodel has whitish-yellow flowers, in short spikes which open between June and August. It has grass-like or sword-shaped leaves that are arranged in a tufted clump. The height of this plant ranges from 8 to 20 cm.

It grows in marshes, damp meadows, wet sandy places and mountain streamsides, preferring calcareous soils. In Britain it is a rare plant of mountains in northern England and Scotland at altitudes up to 1000 m. It is found in northern Europe and eastwards to the central Urals, Alps, Carpathians, east Siberia and arctic North America.

D. K. Mardon

Alpine Speedwell *Veronica alpina*

Alpine Speedwell is between 2 and 15 cm tall. Its oval leaves are sometimes toothed. There are normally 4 – 12 flowers in a compact terminal spike; they are usually dull blue, or occasionally white or reddish in colour. In wet weather the flowers close with the result that this plant is often overlooked in damp mountain areas. The flowering period is July – August.

Stony places, meadows, grasslands, snowbeds, and brooksides are all suitable habitats for this plant. It grows on both acid and base-rich soils. This species has a broad distribution including arctic Europe, Scandinavia, northern Russia, the Faeroes, Iceland, Greenland, Manchuria and north-east Canada. In Britain it is confined to damp alpine rocks in central Scotland, at altitudes between 490 – 1130 m.

D. K. Mardon

Rock Speedwell *Veronica fruticans*

Rock Speedwell flowers between July and August. The flowers last only a short time, often only one day. Its petals are usually vivid blue, but may rarely be white or pink. The presence of white anthers and a purplish-red ring in the middle of the flower may guide insects to the nectaries. This plant has a wiry woody stem and grows up to 20 cm tall.

It is found on rocks, ridges, ledges, and heaths, most abundantly on sunny dry south-facing scree slopes, preferably on base-rich soils. In Britain it is confined to high mountain rocks above 500 m and has a very local distribution in central Scotland. It grows in arctic Europe from Iceland to Russia, in alpine Europe south to the Pyrenees and the Apennines and also in Greenland.

D. K. Mardon

Alpine Woodsia *Woodsia alpina*

Alpine Woodsia has a short, branched rhizome and tufted fronds. The lance-shaped fronds are divided into short paired toothed leaflets and are generally 3 – 8 cm in length. The sori are circular. It is an alpine species that grows at altitudes of 580 – 920 m. It prefers rock-crevices on base-rich soils, often growing in small fissures on inaccessible sheer rock faces. This species requires relatively low maximum summer temperatures and moderately high rainfall and is particularly susceptible to prolonged periods of drought. It is long lived but very slow growing.

This species declined due to Victorian botanical collectors, but this may have only contributed to a long term natural decline. Alpine Woodsia is a relict species in Britain; it is thought to have had a more numerous and widely ranging population in post-glacial time. Gradually as the climate improved and the vegetation changed over very many centuries, Woodsia became confined to increasingly smaller and more isolated sites. The populations became genetically impoverished and inbred, perhaps making them less adaptable to changes in their environment. This species is listed on Schedule 8 of the Wildlife and Countryside Act (1981) which provides stringent legal protection.

It has a high, northern circum-boreal range, including Iceland, Scandinavia, the Pyrenees and the Alps. In Britain, it is at the edge of its natural range, in a delicate balance with the environment. It is now very rare, restricted to Caernarfonshire and central Scotland.

D. K. Mardon

52

References

Angel, H. *et al*. (1981) *The Natural History of Britain and Ireland*. Michael Joseph Ltd., London.

Barneby, T.P. (1967) *European Alpine Flowers in colour*. Thomas Nelson and Son Ltd., London.

Clapham, A.R., Tutin, T.G. and Moore, E.F. (1987) *Flora of the British Isles*. Third edition. CUP

Clapham, A.R., Tutin, T.G. and Warburg, E.F. (1962) *Flora of the British Isles*. Second edition. CUP

Clapham, A.R., Tutin, T.G. and Warburg, E.F. (1968) *Excursion Flora of the British Isles*. Second edition. CUP

Ellis, R.G. (1983) *Flowering plants of Wales*. National Museum of Wales, Cardiff.

Fitter, A. (1978) *An Atlas of the Wild Flowers of Britain and Northern Europe*. Collins, London.

Gibbons, B. and Brough, P. (1992) *The Hamlyn Photographic Guide to the Wild Flowers of Britain and Northern Europe*. Hamlyn.

Gjærevoll, O. (1990) *Distribution of Norwegian Alpine Plants*. Tapir Publishers, Trondheim.

Gjærevoll, O. and Jørgensen, R. (1978) *Mountain Flowers of Scandinavia*. Third edition. Trondheim

Huxley, A. (1967) *Mountain Flowers in Colour*. Blandford Press, London.

Mardon, D. (editor) (1993) *Ben Lawers*. Fourth Edition. National Trust for Scotland.

Martin, W. K. (1974) *The New Concise British Flora*. Bloomsbury Books, London.

Page, C.N. (1988) *Ferns, Their Habitats in the British and Irish Landscape*. New Naturalist Series, Collins, London.

Parish, D. and Parish, M. (1979) *Wild flowers, a photographic guide*. Blandford Press, Dorset.

Perring, F.H. and Farrell, L. (1983) *British Red Data Books: 1 Vascular Plants*. Second edition, Royal Society for Nature Conservation.

Perring, F.H. and Walters, S.M. (editors) (1962) *Atlas of the British Flora*. B.S.B.I., Thomas Nelson and Son Ltd., London.

Ratcliffe, D. (1977) *Highland Flora*. Highlands and Islands Development Board, Inverness.

Raven, J. and Walters, M. (1956) *Mountain flowers*. Collins, London.

Stace, C.A. (1991) *New Flora of the British Isles*. CUP.

Tutin, T.G. *et al*. (editors) (1964-80) *Flora Europaea 1 - 5*. CUP.

Index